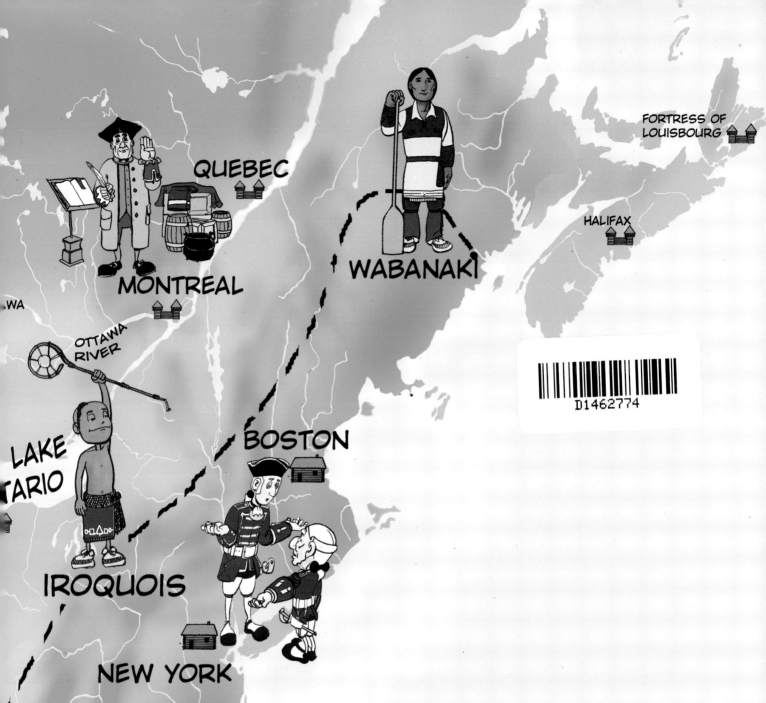

QUEBEC

MONTREAL

WABANAKI

FORTRESS OF LOUISBOURG

HALIFAX

WA

OTTAWA RIVER

LAKE TARIO

IROQUOIS

BOSTON

NEW YORK

THE FRENCH HAVE MOVED INTO THE GREAT LAKES REGION AND ALONG THE ST. LAWRENCE AND OHIO RIVER VALLEYS. TO THE SOUTH EAST, SMALL GROWING POCKETS OF ENGLISH AND EUROPEAN SETTLEMENTS, KNOWN AS THE *13* BRITISH COLONIES, HAVE MOVED INTO THE AREA AS WELL. THE ABORIGINAL COMMUNITIES REMAIN AT PEACE WITH ALL THESE NEW NEIGHBOURS BUT THE GROWING TENSIONS IN THE REGION ARE DISTURBING THAT PEACE AND HARMONY. WHEREVER THEY GO, OUR HEROES, *RABBIT* AND *BEAR PAWS*, ARE PLAYING GAMES ON THE NEIGHBOURS WITH VALUES THAT HAVE SUSTAINED THEIR PEOPLE FOR LIFE.

BOOZHOO (WELCOME) PLEASE COME AND MEET THE FAMILY...

RABBIT, A PINT-SIZED HYPERACTIVE *12*-YEAR-OLD BOY, IS ALWAYS LOOKING FOR SOMETHING FUN AND INTERESTING TO DO. UNFORTUNATELY, RABBIT'S BOLD AND HEADSTRONG NATURE OFTEN GETS HIM INTO TROUBLE. RABBIT IS A LITTLE SMALL FOR HIS AGE BUT WHAT HE LACKS IN STATURE HE MAKES UP FOR IN SPEED WHEN HE RUNS.

BEAR PAWS IS A *10*-YEAR-OLD BOY, A 'LITTLE GIANT' WHO LIKES TO SPEND TIME WITH HIS BROTHER, RABBIT, PLAYING JOKES ON PEOPLE AND ANIMALS. HOWEVER, THESE PRANKS USUALLY BACKFIRE, AND THE BROTHERS OFTEN LEARN THEIR LESSONS THE HARD WAY. BEAR PAWS HAS ALREADY REACHED THE HEIGHT OF A FULL-GROWN MALE, AND CLAIMS TO HAVE THE STRENGTH OF TEN GRIZZLY BEARS, HOWEVER, HE IS NAÏVE AND HAS THE GULLIBILITY TO MATCH. THANKFULLY, HE ALSO USES HIS GIFTS AND TRICKS FOR THE GOOD OF THE PEOPLE.

CLOVER BLOSSOM, ADOPTIVE MOTHER OF BEAR PAWS AND RABBIT, HAS HER HANDS FULL TRYING TO KEEP HER BOYS OUT OF TROUBLE. HER EYESIGHT IS NOT WHAT IT USED TO BE, THOUGH HER POWERFUL VOICE IS AS LOUD AS EVER. ALTHOUGH THE BOYS CAN DRIVE HER CRAZY, SHE LOVES THEM WITH ALL HER HEART - SO MUCH SO, IN FACT, THAT SHE RARELY SUSPECTS THEM OF ANY WRONGDOING.

GREY STONE IS THE ADOPTIVE FATHER OF BEAR PAWS AND RABBIT AND IS ALSO THE VILLAGE MEDICINE MAN. GREY STONE HAS MANY GIFTS AND POWERS. IT ISN'T ALWAYS A GOOD IDEA TO ASK FOR HIS HELP, SINCE HIS MIND OFTEN APPEARS TO BE SOMEWHERE ELSE, MAKING PEOPLE THINK HE'S A LITTLE CRAZY. ONE OF HIS GIFTS IS SPIRIT (CHEEBY) POWDER THAT TRANSFORMS PEOPLE INTO ANIMALS.

...AND NOW ON TO THE ADVENTURES!!!

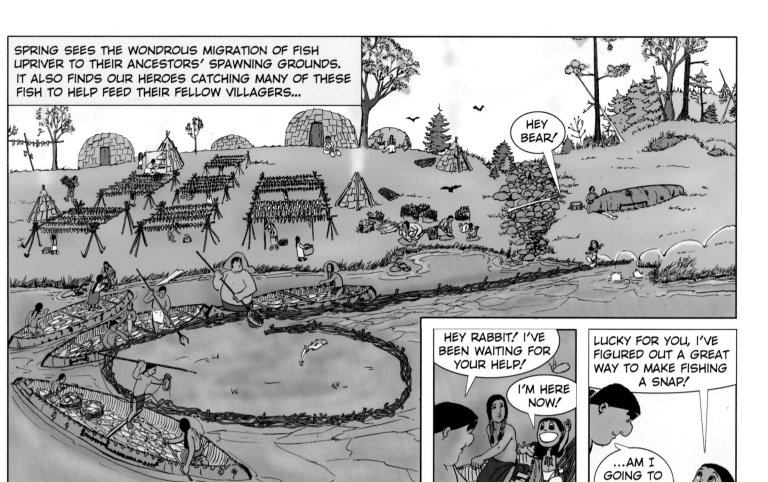

WE'RE REALLY GOING TO A WEDDING? GETTING MARRIED IS THE WORST IDEA EVER!

BELIEVE IT OR NOT, RABBIT, SWAN PROBABLY AGREES WITH YOU.

SO WHY IS SHE GETTING MARRIED?

SHE HASN'T LIKED ANY OF HER SUITORS SO FAR. THIS COMPETITION WILL HELP BY DETERMINING THE STRONGEST, BRAVEST AND WISEST COMPANION FOR HER. IT ACTUALLY REMINDS ME OF THE STORY OF LONE BIRD...

IS IT A STORY ABOUT SMELLY GIRLS?

DON'T BE RUDE!

"LIKE SWAN, LONE BIRD WAS PROUD, STRONG AND BEAUTIFUL. MEN FROM ACROSS THE LAND DESIRED HER HAND IN MARRIAGE."

"BUT EACH SUITOR..."

"REGARDLESS OF THEIR GIFTS..."

"...WAS ROUNDLY REJECTED."

"GOOD FOR HER!"

"SHH, RABBIT!"

9

"WITH LONE BIRD REJECTING HER SUITORS, HER FATHER, DAWN, WAS GROWING CONCERNED."

MY DARLING DAUGHTER! ANY OTHER YOUNG WOMAN WOULD FEEL HONORED WITH THE SUITORS WHO HAVE COME TO WOO YOU.

I'M SORRY, FATHER, BUT I HAVE NO USE FOR A HUSBAND! I HAVE THE LOVE OF YOU AND MOTHER...

...AND THAT IS ALL I NEED.

"HER FATHER DECIDED ON A PLAN: HE WOULD HOLD A RACE. SURELY THE WINNER WOULD BE WORTHY ENOUGH FOR LONE BIRD'S HAND."

"THE RACE WAS HARD-FOUGHT, BUT TWO FRONT-RUNNERS EMERGED: *BENDING BOW* AND *WHO-STRIKES-THE-GAME*."

"THEY ENDED THE RACE IN A TIE! BUT WHO WOULD BE HER HUSBAND?"

"A SECOND RACE WAS HELD THE NEXT DAY, BUT THAT TOO ENDED IN A TIE."

"A JUMPING CONTEST WAS HELD, AND THEN A HUNTING CONTEST. BUT THE TWO WERE EVENLY MATCHED; THERE WAS STILL NO CLEAR WINNER."

"COULD YOU IMAGINE SUCH A THING HAPPENING? MANY ELDERS WONDERED IF THE UNSEEN HAND OF THE GREAT SPIRIT WAS AT WORK."

"BOTH SUITORS WERE TALENTED AND WORTHY, BUT LONE BIRD DID NOT LOVE EITHER OF THEM. SHE PLEADED WITH HER FATHER TO CALL OFF THE TOURNAMENT."

"AND SO HE DID."

"TIME PASSED."

"AS HER PARENTS GREW OLD WITH AGE, SO DID LONE BIRD'S SADNESS GROW DEEPER."

"SHE SAW THAT NOTHING LIVED ALONE: NOT BIRDS, TREES OR EVEN THE ANIMALS."

"BUT WHERE WAS LONE BIRD'S COMPANION? SHE HAD FOUND NONE."

"ALONE BY THE LAKE, SHE COULD ONLY TAKE SOLACE IN THE BEAUTY OF THE MOON OVERHEAD."

"IN THE LIGHT OF THE MOON, LONE BIRD FELT A DEEP CONNECTION THAT HAD ELUDED HER FOR SO LONG."

YOU ARE SO BEAUTIFUL. IF ONLY I HAD YOU TO LOVE, I WOULD NEVER BE LONELY.

"GRANDMOTHER MOON HEARD HER PLEAS, AND SENT HER GRANDSON DOWN. THEY FELL IN LOVE AT FIRST SIGHT."

"WHEN HER PARENTS CAME LOOKING FOR HER, THEY SAW LONE BIRD CRADLED IN THE ARMS OF THE MOON, WITH HER ONE TRUE LOVE."

"SHE SMILED DOWN UPON THEM WITH SUCH WARMTH AND GRACE THAT THEY KNEW SHE WOULD FINALLY BE HAPPY."

WHAT'S THAT, GRANDMOTHER MOON? YOU WANT STRAWBERRY TO COME AND VISIT YOU?

VERY FUNNY, HA HA!

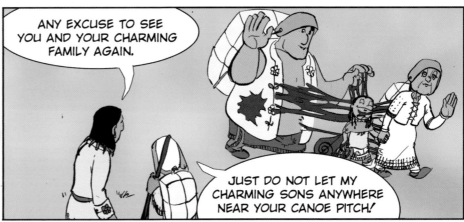

UH... SWAN. HI.

GOOD TO FINALLY SEE YOU AGAIN, SWAYING TREE.

I KNOW I WAS GONE A WHILE...

BUT YOU DECIDED TO COME BACK ONCE I WAS IN DANGER OF MARRYING SOMEONE ELSE?

THAT'S NOT IT. I GUESS THE TIMING IS CONVENIENT, SURE--

WELL, YOU'LL HAVE YOUR CHANCE IN THE RACE TOMORROW MORNING, ALONG WITH ALL THE OTHERS.

I'M SURE YOU'LL DO WELL RUNNING AWAY FROM ME.

JUST FOR THE FIRST HALF. THEN I'LL BE RUNNING RIGHT BACK TO YOU.

NICE WORDS. BUT YOU'RE GOING TO NEED MORE THAN THAT, SWAYING TREE... MUCH MORE.

SWAN? ARE YOU OK?

I'M SORRY... NOW ISN'T A GOOD TIME...

LET ME ENJOY MY TIME ALONE WHILE I STILL HAVE IT...

BEELLLCH!!

NICE ONE!

ARGH!... GUYS!

14

GRANDMOTHER MOON?... IT'S ME AGAIN. I WAS HOPING I COULD GET SOME ADVICE.

IT'S JUST... I'VE NEVER REALLY *LOVED* ANY OF MY SUITORS, YOU KNOW? I DON'T WANT TO MARRY SOMEONE I DO NOT LOVE. I CAN'T HELP HOW I FEEL.

TRUE, THERE WAS SWAYING TREE, BUT...

I MEAN, WILL I EVER FIND SOMEONE? SHOULD I JUST ACCEPT TOMORROW'S WINNER AS MY HUSBAND? SHOULD I RUN AWAY?... GRANDMOTHER MOON, WON'T YOU GIVE ME AN ANSWER?

PLEASE?

THE NEXT MORNING...

KITCHI MANITOU*, GUIDE AND PROTECT THESE MEN ON THEIR JOURNEY...RUNNERS! GET READY...

* GREAT SPIRIT

...GET SET...
GO!!

THIS IS SO EXCITING! I CAN'T BELIEVE RABBIT AND BEAR PAWS ARE MISSING THIS!

I'M NOT SURE THEIR SHORT ATTENTION SPANS COULD HANDLE THE STRAIN.

15

SURE ENOUGH, NOT TOO FAR AWAY...

TAG! YOU'RE IT!

AW, MAN!

WANNA PLAY AGAIN?

YEAH, BUT WE REALLY NEED MORE THAN TWO OF US FOR A GOOD GAME OF TAG.

WE COULD ASK STRAWBERRY TO JOIN US!

EWW, NO WAY! SHE'D PROBABLY GIVE US FLEAS OR SOMETHING.

COME ON, RABBIT. I KNOW HOW YOU REALLY FEEL ABOUT HER!

WHAT'S THAT SUPPOSED TO MEAN?! SHE'S ICKY AND SHE SMELLS FUNNY AND I HEARD SHE LIKES TO MAKE BABIES CRY...

AND HER HAIR'S ALL DIRTY AND SHE HAS A TERRIBLE SENSE OF FASHION AND SHE SNEERS A LOT AND WHY ARE YOU LOOKING AT ME LIKE THAT??

AGH! STRAWBERRY?

I THOUGHT YOU TWO MIGHT LIKE A DRINK!

UH... REALLY?... WHAT DID YOU DO TO THE WATER?

WELL, LOOK WHO'S A SCAREDY-CAT! HERE, I'LL HAVE SOME.

GAAK! HELP! POISON!!

AAAAHHHHHH!!!

HAH! GOTCHA!

HA! HA!

HEY! JERK...

MEEGWETCH, STRAWBERRY! YOU WANT TO PLAY HIDE-AND-SEEK WITH US?

I'D LOVE TO!

WHAT ARE YOU DOING??

SHE'S A GOOD GIRL! BE NICE TO HER OR I'LL TELL MOM.

YOU WOULDN'T!

NEXT, THE *ARROW RETRIEVAL*...

THE WINNER OF THE SECOND TRIAL IS *RABBIT!*

AS IT SHOULD BE*!*

NEXT, THE TEST OF WISDOM...

"WHAT RUNS BUT NEVER WALKS, HAS A MOUTH BUT NEVER TALKS, HAS A BED BUT NEVER SLEEPS?"

UH... SOMEONE WITH SOME SERIOUS PROBLEMS?

I KNOW THIS, I KNOW THIS... WAIT, DON'T TELL ME... SERIOUSLY, I *KNOW* THIS...

RUNS BUT NEVER WALKS? YOU MEAN *RABBIT?*

"...HAS A BED, BUT NEVER SLEEPS?"... THE ANSWER IS ...A RIVER.

WHITE OWL WINS THE THIRD TRIAL!

OH YEAH, GOOD ANSWER. I STILL LIKED *MY* ANSWER BETTER...

WITH THE FOUR TRIALS OVER, EVERYONE RETURNS TO THE VILLAGE...

WITH THE CONTESTANTS IN A FOUR-WAY TIE, THERE IS NO CLEAR WINNER OF THE COMPETITION. THE ELDERS MUST DELIBERATE UPON THIS TONIGHT, AND WILL ANNOUNCE A WINNER TOMORROW MORNING.

WELL, THAT WAS ANTI-CLIMACTIC.

I *KNEW* IT WASN'T A GOOD IDEA TO GET INVOLVED IN THIS!

IT WOULD'VE BEEN THE SAME WITHOUT US.

I MEAN, YOU'D THINK THERE WOULD AT LEAST BE AN *ODD* NUMBER OF EVENTS.

YEAH, NO KIDDING!

MY BOYS. HOW CAN YOU TWO GET INTO SO MUCH TROUBLE?

MOM! AREN'T YOU PROUD OF US?

PROUD? DO YOU BOYS EVEN KNOW WHAT YOU'VE GOTTEN YOURSELVES INTO?

BEAR PAWS, DO YOU REALLY WISH TO GET *MARRIED* AT YOUR AGE?

WELL...

DO YOU, RABBIT?

BUT MOM, I HAVE A CHANCE TO *WIN!*

HAVE YOU THOUGHT ABOUT *WHAT* YOU'RE WINNING? WHY IS IT SO IMPORTANT TO YOU?

BECAUSE IF I WIN, I'LL BE THE *BEST!*

YOUTH...

AT DINNER, THE 4 FINALISTS ARE TREATED LIKE HONOURED GUESTS...

PLEASE ENJOY THE FINEST OF OUR MEATS!

MEEGWETCH!

...BUT FOR MOST OF THEM, *FOOD* IS NOT THE TOP PRIORITY.

MMM! RABBIT, YOU SHOULD TRY THE VENISON ... RABBIT?

YES, RABBIT, *LITTLE CHILDREN* NEED TO EAT TO GROW UP!

AH, SOME NEED MORE THAN FOOD TO GAIN WISDOM! SOME ARE JUST NOT *MEANT* FOR MARRIAGE.

LOOK HERE. I AM OBVIOUSLY THE BEST AND *ONLY* POTENTIAL HUSBAND HERE.

AND *MODEST!*

IT'S TRUE. I CAN PROVIDE FOR SWAN BETTER THAN ANY OF YOU. ISN'T THAT WHAT THIS IS ALL ABOUT? HOW WILL YOU *CHILDREN* PROVIDE FOR HER?

YOU CAN'T, OF COURSE! BUT WHEN THE ELDERS REALIZE I CAN, THEY WILL AWARD ME SWAN'S HAND IN MARRIAGE! AND THEN I WILL BE KNOWN AND RESPECTED ACROSS THE LAND!

UH... YEAH, WELL...THAT, UH, REMINDS ME...

I GOTTA GO DO SOMETHING, SEE YOU GUYS LATER!

RABBIT?

24

WHAT ARE YOU DOING?

JUST WHITTLING AWAY THE TIME. I DON'T HAVE MUCH ELSE TO DO WITH IT ANYMORE.

I HEARD YOU WERE FAR AHEAD UP UNTIL THE... ACCIDENT.

I WAS. IT'S A SHAME, BUT WHAT CAN YOU DO?

I'M SURE YOU'LL BE VERY HAPPY WITH WHOMEVER THE ELDERS PICK.

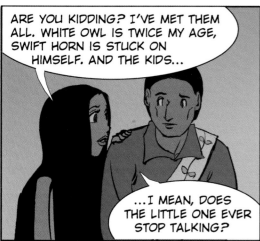

ARE YOU KIDDING? I'VE MET THEM ALL. WHITE OWL IS TWICE MY AGE, SWIFT HORN IS STUCK ON HIMSELF. AND THE KIDS...

...I MEAN, DOES THE LITTLE ONE EVER STOP TALKING?

HEY...!

I NEVER WANTED THIS COMPETITION! WHY SHOULD I WANT MY HUSBAND DECIDED BY SOME *RACE*?

I SEEM TO REMEMBER GIVING YOU ANOTHER OPTION BEFORE IT EVEN BEGAN, BUT YOU WOUDN'T HEAR OF IT.

SOMETIMES, UNFORTUNATELY, WE INJURE OURSELVES WITH OUR OWN GIFTS.

YOU AND I HAVE ALWAYS BEEN PROUD -- BUT TOO PROUD TO ADMIT OUR FAULTS...AND NOW, MAYBE IT'S TOO LATE FOR US.

BUT FOR WHAT IT'S WORTH, I'M SORRY FOR ABANDONING YOU ALL THOSE YEARS. AND I'M SORRY FOR EXPECTING YOU TO BRUSH IT OFF LIKE A DAY OF BAD WEATHER.

SWAYING TREE--

YOU STILL LIKE TO HUNT, DON'T YOU?

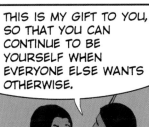

RABBIT? WHAT ARE YOU DOING HERE?

HE'S COME TO INFLUENCE OUR DECISION!

LEAVE NOW, YOUNG MAN!

WAIT, MY BROTHERS. RABBIT HAS AS GOOD A HEART AS ANY OF US. RABBIT, PLEASE EXPLAIN YOUR REASON FOR THE INTERRUPTION.

OKAY, SEE - YOU SHOULDN'T CHOOSE *ANY* OF US! NONE OF US WOULD BE GOOD FOR SWAN. WE WERE ALL SO WRAPPED UP IN WINNING THAT WE DIDN'T REALLY THINK ABOUT HER.

SWAN REALLY WANTS TO MARRY SWAYING TREE, ANYWAY.

NONSENSE. SHE WOULDN'T EVEN SPEAK TO HIM BEFORE THE RACE! SHE'S BEING IMPULSIVE AS ALWAYS.

NO - SHE'S JUST COMPLICATED. BUT SHE AND SWAYING TREE KNOW THEY LOVE EACH OTHER, AND IF WE DON'T HURRY THEY'RE GOING TO RUN AWAY TOGETHER AND WE'LL NEVER SEE THEM AGAIN!!

SWAN! SWAYING TREE!

GOING SOMEWHERE?

UH... YES, ACTUALLY. SWAN AND I HAVE DECIDED THAT--

WE KNOW WHAT YOU HAVE DECIDED.

YOU ALREADY KNOW?

YES, THANKS TO RABBIT.

AND NOW, WE HAVE TO STOP YOU FROM MAKING A MISTAKE!

OUR LOVE IS NOT A MISTAKE!

WE KNOW. AND THAT IS WHY WE APPROVE OF YOUR MARRIAGE.

BUT YOU-- WAIT, WHAT?

YOU *APPROVE?*

WE CAN'T HAVE YOU RUNNING AWAY! THE ELDERS WILL ACCEPT SWAYING TREE AS YOUR HUSBAND, IF THAT IS WHAT YOU TRULY WANT.

YES, I DO!

WE DO.

AND THAT'S THE FIRST THING WE'VE AGREED ON IN YEARS.

TO THINK HOW CLOSE I CAME TO NEVER SEEING YOU AGAIN!

YOU SHOULD ALSO THANK RABBIT. HE SHOWED US THE SITUATION IN A WAY WE HADN'T CONSIDERED.

REALLY?

I MEAN, IT'S LIKE THE STORY OF LONE BIRD, RIGHT? LOVE DOESN'T ALWAYS HAPPEN THE WAY YOU EXPECT. AND IF YOU TRY TO FORCE IT... THINGS WON'T WORK OUT.

THANK YOU SO MUCH, RABBIT. YOU DID A BRAVE AND SELFLESS THING.

IT'S THE LEAST I COULD DO AFTER WE KIND OF CHEATED OUR WAY INTO THE WINNER'S CIRCLE.

YOU *WHAT??*

I MEAN, UH... NOTHING?

THE NEXT DAY.

FAREWELL MY BROTHERS AND SISTERS! MAY THE GREAT SPIRIT GUIDE YOU HOME SAFELY.

FAREWELL, OLD FRIEND. THINGS ARE ALWAYS MORE INTERESTING WHEN YOU AND YOUR FAMILY VISIT.

MEEGWETCH.

TO THINK, I COULD HAVE HAD THE PRETTIEST GIRL AROUND!

SNIFF!

SNIFF!

SEE YOU SOON!

THANKS AGAIN!

WHAT A TRIP!

INDEED!... STRAWBERRY, COULD YOU GIVE OUR BOYS A MESSAGE?

SURE!

TELL THEM THEY CAN REST AT THE TOP OF THE HILL!

YOUR PARENTS SAID NO REST UNTIL SUNDOWN!

MAN! THIS IS THEIR HEAVIEST LESSON YET!

THE END!

32